CHILDREN'S FAVORITE
STORIES
& SONGS

THIS BOOK BELONGS TO:

_____

ISBN: 9781569191132
Printed in China

Cover and interior illustrations by Tim O'Connor
Cover and interior design by Jay Elkins

HOW TO DOWNLOAD THE 100 SONGS-
1. Go to www.wonderkidsplayer.com
2. Enter the Code: CFSS100
3. Enjoy!

TABLE OF CONTENTS

THE CAT AND THE FIDDLE

Hey diddle diddle
The cat and the fiddle
The cow jumped over the moon.

The little dog laughed
To see such sport,
And the dish ran away
With the spoon.

THERE WAS AN OLD WOMAN

There was an old woman
Who lived in a shoe.

She had so many children
She didn't know what to do.

She gave them some porridge
And sweet gingerbread;

And kissed each one softly
And put them to bed.

THE LION AND THE MOUSE

One day little Mousey
was walking the trail,
when a hungry ole Lion
snatched him up by the tail!

"Well, well, well," said the Lion,
"what's this I see?
Could it be lunch is delivered to me?"

"Oh my," said Mousey, "hear me today!
Don't eat me Mr. Lion,
there's a much better way!
Spare me, I beg you,
spare me, please do
and one day I promise
I'll come rescue you!"

"I know I'm itty bitty,
and not very strong.
But you never know
what trouble might come along.

So if you will spare me,
I promise, cross my heart
to come to your rescue,
if trouble should start!"

"Ha, ha, ha," said the lion,
"little you... help BIG me?
What could you do?
What would it be?

Lunch sounds much better,
but thanks for the thought."
Then suddenly it happened,
Mr. Lion was caught!

"Help!" cried the Lion, from inside a net.
"Don't worry!" said Mousey,
"It's not over yet!
My teeth are like razors, made to chew!
I'll bite through this rope,
in a minute or two!"

"Chew little Mousey,
in these ropes I am bound!"
Then Mousey broke through,
and Lion fell to the ground!

"You did it!" cried Mr. Lion. "You did indeed!
Little ole you saved great BIG ole me!"

Now Mr. Lion and Mousey
were so glad they'd met.
They both learned
a lesson they
will never forget.

No matter how big,
no matter how small
We all need a friend,
on whom we can call!

THE ANT AND
THE GRASSHOPPER

It happened on a warm summer day. A family of busy ants was cleaning house. Scrub-a-dub-dub they mopped and hopped all over that house making sure it was clean.

Just then Grasshopper skated by. "Why do you work", he asked with a smirk. "I like to play all day, so don't even get in my way!"

After cleaning the house, the ants worked on the outside. They made their house strong and fixed all the holes in the roof.

But Grasshopper just sat in the yard and played cards with the caterpillar. "No work for me," he said. "I'd rather play instead!"

"One day you'll be sorry," said the ant as a warning. "Winter is coming and what will you do? You better start working before the snow covers you!"

COMING SOON!
ANT HILL
ESTATES

"Work?" said the Grasshopper, "not me, no, not me! The sun is out, the sky is blue. And there are a thousand fun things to do!"

Time passed
and soon the
chilly winter wind
began to blow.

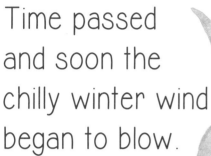

The ant family
went into their
home. It was
warm and
clean. The roof
was strong and
the outside walls
held back the
snow.

But what about Grasshopper?
He had no place to go. No
wood to burn, no food to
eat. Not even socks
on his cold
frozen feet!

So he knocked on the door of the ant family. Daddy ant opened the door. He saw that Grasshopper was cold and weary.

"Can I come in?" asked Grasshopper. "I'm so hungry and cold." "I'm so sorry," said the ant. "I warned you of this. I only have enough for my family and me. Those who act wisely prepare for winter. But the foolish play and play every day."

"There's a time to work... and a time to play! So sorry Grasshopper, be on your way!"

THE TORTOISE AND THE HARE

Rabbit just wanted to run
So he asked the ole Turtle just for fun
"Would you come and race me today?
I bet I can beat you, what do you say?"

Turtle knew his pace was slow
But still he'd try his best you know
So off they went, and wouldn't you know
Turtle really was slow, slow, slow!

Rabbit was leading the race by a mile
So he stopped to rest his feet a while
But Turtle kept going, his eye on the prize
And as Rabbit slept, Turtle passed him by!

But Rabbit woke up, only to find
Turtle was crossing the red finish line!
So he jumped up and ran
like a greased lightning bolt
But he tripped,
and fell on his face with a jolt.

Turtle had won the race!
He won with his slow and steady pace.
He gave his all and passed the test,
Turtle won the race by doing his best!

PINOCCHIO

Geppetto was a carpenter. He made
wooden toys for the children of his village.
One day, he made a wooden puppet.
He named him Pinocchio.

Geppetto wished his wooden puppet was
a real boy. That night something magical
happened! Pinocchio came to life and began
to walk and talk, just like a real boy!

Geppetto treated his new son with love and kindness. He told Pinocchio to always be truthful and loving to everyone. But Pinocchio didn't listen to Geppetto. He began to tell little lies that turned into bigger and bigger lies.

As Pinocchio's lies got bigger, his nose grew bigger too! Lying is not a good thing to do. So his friends stopped believing what Pinocchio said. He found himself alone, without any friends,

Pinocchio was sorry for what he had done. So
he changed. He decided to always tell the truth!
All his friends forgave him! His nose shrank to
it's normal size and he was so happy.

Geppetto was proud of his son! That's because the truth is always the best thing to tell! Geppetto and Pinocchio lived happily ever after.

PETER PIPER

Peter Piper picked a peck
Of pickled peppers.
A peck of pickled peppers
Peter Piper picked.

If Peter Piper picked a peck
Of pickled peppers,
Where's the peck of pickled peppers
Peter Piper picked?

BAA, BAA, BLACKSHEEP

Baa, Baa, black sheep
Have you any wool?
Yes, sir. Yes, sir.
Three bags full.

One for the master.
One for the dame.
And one for the little boy
Who lives down the lane.

HOT CROSS BUNS

Hot cross buns!
Hot cross buns!
One a penny, two a penny,
Hot cross buns!

If you have no daughters,
Give them to your sons.
One a penny, two a penny,
Hot cross buns.

ON A COLD AND FROSTY MORNING

Here we go round
The mulberry bush,
The mulberry bush,
The mulberry bush.

Here we go round
The mulberry bush,
On a cold and
Frosty morning.

This is the way we
Wash our hands,
Wash our hands,
Wash our hands.

This is the way we
Wash our hands,
On a cold and frosty morning.

This is the way we
Wash our clothes,
Wash our clothes,
Wash our clothes.

This is the way
We wash our clothes,
On a cold and
Frosty morning.

SEE SAW

See Saw,
Margery Daw,
Johnny shall have
A new master;

He shall have
But a penny a day,
Because he can't work
Any faster.

THE BOY WHO CRIED WOLF

Once, a shepherd,
thought to be
a truthful boy,
so trustworthy
decided he'd be
bad and cry,
"Help, a wolf!"
But it was a lie.

His teeth are long,
his eyes are mean.
He's the meanest
wolf I've ever seen!

And when he growls
the sheep all run.
Come quickly before
we're all done!

When all the people heard his shout,
they grabbed their sticks to help him out.
Running up hills so rough and steep
they ran to save the little sheep.

But when they'd climbed the rocky hill,
there was no wolf, all was calm and still.
Where's the wolf? Why did you call?
We don't see a wolf at all!

"There is no wolf, it's just a trick.
I knew you'd come with rake and stick."
He laughed and laughed 'til he almost cried.
But it isn't funny telling lies.

"You shouldn't fib and call it fun.
What If a wolf had really come?"
"O lighten up, enjoy the day."
Then all the people went away.

That was fun, to fool the crowd.
I'll do it again, then laugh out loud.
So he let out a yell, so loud and clear
"The wolf is back! He's really here!

His mouth is snarled
his face is mean.
He's the biggest wolf
I've ever seen!

He's about to
pounce upon
my flock.
Come save
us, run! And
do not stop!"

You could hear laughter from summit to summit.
But it wasn't a joke, no far far from it!
The people walked away, hot under their collars.
He won't fool me again. I won't come if he hollers.

But suddenly, in the wink of an eye,
everything changed, and do you know why?
Because out from the bushes stepped
a critter so mean; "It's a wolf!" cried the
shepherd, "it's a wolf that I've seen!"

The shepherd boy shouted
at the top of his lungs,
"The WOLF is here, please,
everyone come!
I'm telling the truth,"
he said with a cry.
But nobody listened,
thinking it was a lie.

They all stayed at home,
I can't blame them at all.
While the wolf ate his dinner,
they heard the boy call.
This lesson we learn,
I'll share it with you:
Telling the truth
is the best thing to do!

1,2,3,4 AND EVEN MORE!

1,2
One, two,
Buckle my shoe.

3,4
Three, four,
Open the door

5,6
Five, six,
Pick up sticks.

7,8
Seven, eight,
Lay them straight.

9,10
Nine, ten,
A big fat hen.

11,12
Eleven, twelve
Dig and delve.

13,14

Thirteen, fourteen
Maids a-courting.

15,16

Fifteen, sixteen
Maids in the kitchen.

17,18

Seventeen, eighteen
Maids a-waiting.

19,20

Nineteen, twenty
My plates empty.

TOM, TOM THE PIPERS SON

Tom, Tom,
The piper's son,
Stole a pig,
And away he run.

But the pig had feet,
And Tom was beat,
And Tom went crying
Down the street.

THE DONKEY

Donkey, Donkey, old and grey,
Open your mouth and gently bray.

Lift your ears and blow your horn,
To wake the world this sleepy morn.

LiTTLE BiRD

Little Bird, little bird,
You joyfully fly!
You're so very happy.
Please tell me why!

"I have something special,"
The Little Bird peeped.
"I have a nest,
A soft place to sleep!

Would you like to see it?
It's a nest made for me.
It's down in the meadow
Way up in a tree."

When Mr. Bear saw it
He smiled then said,
"Be thankful you have
A soft little bed!"

HUMPTY DUMPTY

Humpty Dumpty sat on a wall.
Humpty Dumpty had a great fall.
All the kings horses,
And all the king's men,
Couldn't put Humpty together again.

JACK BE NIMBLE

Jack be nimble.
Jack be quick.
Jack jump over
The candlestick.

LITTLE MISS MUFFET

Little Miss Muffet
Sat on her tuffet,
Eating her curds and whey.

Along came a spider,
That sat down beside her,
And frightened Miss Muffet away!

OLD MOTHER HUBBARD

Old Mother Hubbard
Went to the cupboard
To fetch her poor dog a bone.

But when she got there
The cupboard was bare,
And so her poor dog had none.

THIS LITTLE PIG

This little piggy went to market.
This little piggy stayed home.
This little piggy had roast beef.
And this little piggy had none.

But THIS little piggy
Went WEE-WEE-WEE
All the way home!

THE DANCING ELEPHANT

I once saw a lion
Jump through rings of fire.
I've watched a striped tiger
Walk high on a wire.

But this, like no other,
Amazes me so:
An elephant dancing
In an orange tuxedo!

Quiet Please

'FRAIDY CAT

He's frightened by noises
And most any sound.
He's scared of his shadow
That follows him 'round.

Afraid of a mouse
It's a terrible shame!
Who could it be?
'Fraidy Cat is his name!

THREE LITTLE KITTENS

Three little kittens,
They lost their mittens,
And they began to cry,
"Oh, mother dear, we sadly fear,
Our mittens we have lost."

"What! Lost your mittens,
You naughty kittens!
Then you shall have no pie."
"Meow, meow, meow."

The three little kittens,
They found their mittens,
And they began to cry,
"Oh, mother dear, see here, see here,
Our mittens we have found."

"Put on your mittens,
you silly kittens,
And you shall have some pie."
"Purr, purr, purr."

MARY HAD A LITTLE LAMB

Mary had a little Lamb,
It's fleece was white as snow;
And everywhere that Mary went,
The lamb was sure to go.

It followed her to school one day,
Which was against the rule.
It made the children laugh and play,
To see a lamb at school.

And so the teacher sent it out,
But still it lingered near.
And waited patiently about,
'Til Mary did appear.

"What makes the lamb love Mary so?"
The happy children cry.
"Why, Mary loves the lamb you know!"
The teacher did reply.

RAIN, RAIN, GO AWAY

Rain, rain,
Go away,
Come again
Another day.

Rain, rain,
Go away
For the children
Want to play.

RUB A DUB DUB

Rub a dub dub,
Three men in a tub;
And who do you think they be?
The butcher, the baker,
The candlestick maker;
All put out to sea.

HICKORY DICKORY DOCK

Hickory dickory dock,
A mouse ran up the clock.
The clock struck one,
The mouse ran down;
Hickory, dickory dock.

ROCK-A-BYE BABY

Rock-a-bye baby,
In the tree top;
When the wind blows,
The cradle will rock;

When the bough breaks,
The cradle will fall;
And down will come baby,
Cradle and all.

LITTLE BOY BLUE

Little boy blue,
Come blow your horn;
The sheep's in the meadow,
The cow's in the corn.

And where's the boy
Who looks after the sheep?
Under the haystack,
Fast asleep!

WEE WILLIE WINKIE

Wee Willie Winkie
Runs through the town.
Upstairs and downstairs,
In his nightgown.

Rapping at the window,
Crying through the lock;
"Are the children in their beds?
Now it's eight o'clock."

PEASE PORRIDGE HOT

Pease porridge hot,
Pease porridge cold,
Pease porridge in the pot,
Nine days old.

115

Some like it hot.
Some like it cold
Some like it in the pot,
Nine days old.

GOOSEY, GOOSEY, GANDER

Goosey, goosey, gander,
Where do you wander?
Upstairs and downstairs
And then over yonder.

Goosey Goosey Gander
To the pool meander
Spring, Sprong, Jump so long
No one can understand her!

LITTLE BO PEEP

Little Bo Peep
Has lost her sheep,
And doesn't know where
To find them.

Leave them alone,
And they'll come home,
Wagging their tails
Behind them.

OLD MOTHER GOOSE

Old Mother Goose's friends,
When they want to wander,
Would ride through the air
On a very fine gander.

Old Mother Goose
Took her friends for ride
High above the pretty clouds
They would glide... glide... GLIDE!

FIDDLE-DE-DEE

Fiddle-de-dee,
Fiddle-de-dee,
The fly has married
The bumblebee.

The wedding was
Such a sight to see,
I only wish
They'd invited me.

I SAW A SHIP-A-SAILING

I saw a ship-a-sailing,
A-sailing on the sea;
And oh it was so laden
With pretty things indeed!

There was candy in the cabin
And apples in the hold;
The sails were made of silk,
And the masts were made of gold.

The four-and-twenty sailors
That stood between the decks,
Were four-and-twenty little mice
With bands about their necks.

The captain was a duck,
With a packet on his back;
And when the ship began to move,
The captain said, "Quack! Quack!"

JACK AND JILL

Jack and Jill went up the hill,
To fetch a pail of water.
Jack fell down and broke his crown,
And Jill came tumbling after.

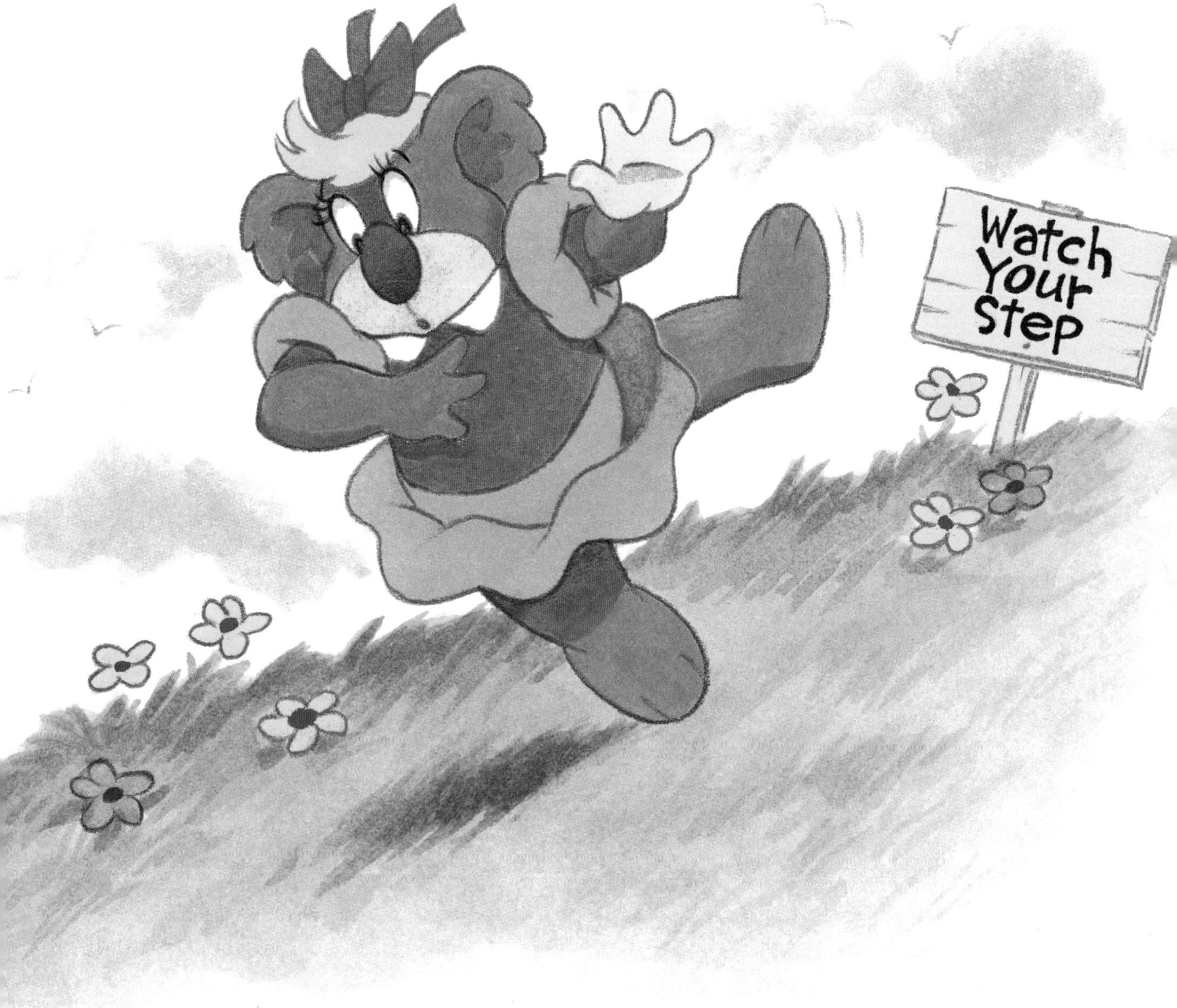
Watch Your Step

THE FOUR SEASONS

Spring time brings us
Lots of showers.

While Summer gives us
Pretty flowers.

With Autumn comes
A colorful show.

And Winter brings
The ice and snow.

POLLY PUT A KETTLE ON

Polly put the kettle on,
And let's drink tea.
Sukey take it off again,
They're all gone away.

RING AROUND THE ROSIES

Ring around the rosies,
Pocket full of posies,
Ashes, ashes,
We all fall down.